Chicken Licken

Written by Gill Munton

Illustrated by Christine Pym

OXFORD

UNIVERSITY PRESS

Tock!

2

3

Chicken Licken ran to the barn.

Chicken Licken and Hen Len
ran to the farmyard.

They all ran back to the garden.

13

Once upon a time...

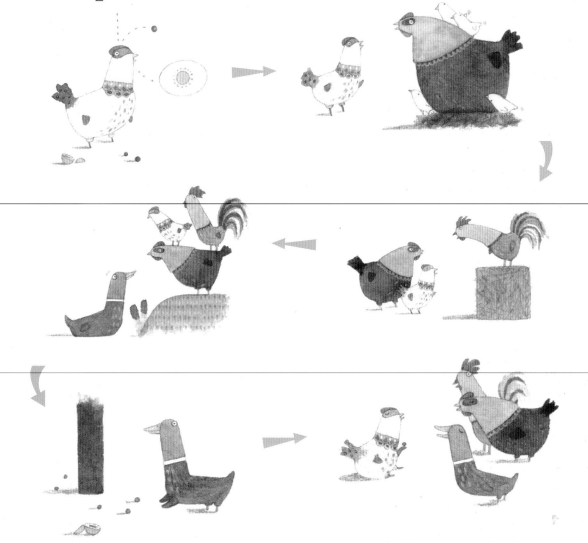

The end.